GW00992786

Little Grey Rabbit to the Rescue

A Play

Alison Uttley
pictures by Margaret Tempest

Collins

William Collins Sons & Co Ltd
London · Glasgow · Sydney · Auckland
Toronto · Johannesburg

First published 1945
© text The Alison Uttley Literary Property Trust 1945 and 1970
© illustrations The Estate of Margaret Tempest 1988
© this arrangement William Collins Sons & Co Ltd 1988
Cover decoration by Fiona Owen

ISBN 0 00 194287-5

Made and printed in Great Britain by
William Collins Sons & Co Ltd, Glasgow

CHARACTERS

Little Grey Rabbit
Hare
Squirrel
Milkman Hedgehog
Weasel

Play in three short scenes
with music for Hare's song

Patterns to make the characters in this play can be found in
Little Grey Rabbit's Pattern Book by Pamela Peake

FOREWORD

You can act this play with your friends. There are five characters – Squirrel, Hare, Hedgehog, Weasel and Little Grey Rabbit.

In the book, *Little Grey Rabbit's Pattern Book*, there are patterns for making these five characters and their clothes. The toys can act the parts and you can speak the words.

Or you can act the parts yourselves, dressing up in the sort of clothes the animals wore.

A little wooden box will do for the Lavender tea.

The oven in the Weasel's house can be a cardboard box painted black. The flaps on the box will be the oven door. You can paint red flames to represent the fire in the fireplace.

If you act this play in autumn you can have real sycamore keys, but at other times of the year you must make from green paper the bunch of fruit from the sycamore tree.

SCENE ONE

SCENE: *The interior of Little Grey Rabbit's kitchen. It is a cosy little room, with bright rugs on the floor. The window at the back of the stage has blue check curtains and frills. There are red geraniums flowering in pots on the window-sill.*

On the right stands the dresser, with blue and white mugs and brown teapot, and yellow baking bowls and flour bin. On the left is the open fireplace, with kettle on hob, and porridge saucepan. A fender is in front of the fire, a clock on the mantelpiece, a pair of china dogs, and candlesticks. In the middle of the room the table is set for breakfast, with a white cloth, mugs and plates, and a jug of flowers in the centre. At the back, near the window, is a door going to the staircase. On the extreme right a door leading to the outside woods and fields.

SQUIRREL *sits at the table, beating time with
her wooden spoon, swaying to and fro in the
rocking chair. She is dressed in her spotted pink
dress.*

SQUIRREL (calling): Grey Rabbit – Grey
Rabbit – Grey Rabbit . . .

The stairway door opens and HARE *comes in,
dressed in his brown dressing-gown. He potters
round the room, looks at the table,
lifts the lid from a pot, peers
into the saucepan on the
fire, dances a step or two with
his dressing-gown held out. Then
sinks down in the big
chair at the table, and
raps with his spoon.*

HARE: Grey Rabbit! Grey Rabbit!
Bring me,
Lavender tea.
SQUIRREL (*calling in a high voice*):
Grey Rabbit, Grey Rabbit, what are
you doing?
The kettle is boiling, the tea should
be brewing.
HARE: Grey Rabbit, Grey Rabbit, come
along quick
And stir up the porridge, or else it will stick.
HARE and SQUIRREL (*singing together, tune of*
"*Mulberry Bush*"):

Bring me, Lavender Tea,
Lavender Tea, Lavender Tea.
Bring me, Lavender Tea,
this fine and frosty morning.

GREY RABBIT *comes running in from door on right. She carries a small square wooden chest with* LAVENDER TEA *painted in large letters upon it. In her hand is a bunch of keys of every size and kind – large door keys, watch keys, etc. She wears her grey dress with blue apron, white collar and cuffs.*

She drops the keys with a clatter on the floor, and puts the tea chest on the table with the name facing the audience.

GREY RABBIT:

The Lavender Tea is locked in the chest.
I'm sorry I'm late but I've done my best.
I've tried the key of the cottage front door,
Hare's watch key, the clock key, but
never before
Has the tea chest resisted my own furry paw.
Even the key of the old money-box
Will not unfasten these rusty old locks.
Letter-box, cupboard and larder too,
I've tried their keys but it *won't* undo.

SQUIRREL (*running to window and pointing out*):
  There are plenty of them in the sycamore trees.
  The branches are cluttered with little green keys.
GREY RABBIT:
  Please, dearest Squirrel, please get some for me,
  For nobody else can climb up a tree.
  Please, darling Squirrel, will you tuck up your frock
  And get sycamore keys to unfasten my lock?
SQUIRREL:
  All right, Grey Rabbit, I'll climb up a bough
  And get you a bunch of ripe sycamore now.

(*She runs out of the house door, tucking up her skirt as she goes.* HARE *rocks to and fro at the table, beating with his spoon.*)

HARE (*chanting*):

I want my breakfast, I want my dinner.
I'm very hungry, I'm getting thinner.

GREY RABBIT (*stirring porridge at the fire*):

Oh, Hare! Oh, Hare! Take care, take care.

HARE:

Bacon and porridge, coffee and tea,
There's nothing to eat that I can see.

GREY RABBIT (*fetching food from the dresser and putting it on the table*):

Cobnuts for Squirrel (*puts a bowl of nuts in* SQUIRREL'S *place*),

Lettuce for Hare (*puts leaves of lettuce on* HARE'S *plate. He begins to eat, hungrily*).
A carrot for Rabbit (*she puts a red carrot on her own plate*).
But nothing to spare,
For the bold postman, Robin, and gay
Tom-tit,
Who wait in the garden for their little bit.
(*Runs to window and throws out a crumb.*)
The larder is empty, we've nothing to eat,
There isn't a morsel of green rabbit meat.

HARE:
We must go to the fair with our paws
full of money,
To buy bread and cheese, and a
bottle of honey.

(SQUIRREL *returns with a branch of sycamore,*
with the green fruit keys dangling from it.)
SQUIRREL:
Grey Rabbit, Grey Rabbit, here are
the keys,
Plucked from the boughs of the
sycamore trees.
(GREY RABBIT *takes them and unlocks the*
chest. she puts tea in the pot. SQUIRREL *closes*
the door.)
GREY RABBIT:
Thank you, kind Squirrel, for climbing
that bough.
I can make a good pot of tea for you now.
(*Makes tea and pours out.*)
SQUIRREL (*proudly dancing up and down,*
skirts held out):
I am so clever, the tree was so tall
Nobody else could climb it at all.

Rabbit and Hare never run up the boughs,
Nor sit in the branches and gaze at the cows.
Rabbit and Hare cannot hide in the leaves.
Only Miss Squirrel's at home in the trees.
(*Sits at table.*)

HARE:

I am so swift I can run like the arrow
Shot from the bow of the little cock sparrow.
I have won every race, although old
Æsop said
A Tortoise once beat my own ancestor, dead
These two thousand years in far-away
Greece.

But no one can catch me, not even
the Police.
I am bold, I am brave, I'm a
wonderful Hare,
I can face every danger with never a care. (*He
runs back to the table, eats more lettuce, and
drinks tea.*)
GREY RABBIT:
You both are so wise, I really don't see
Why you e'er came to live with a Rabbit
like me.
I am timid and shy, I couldn't say "Hey"
To a goose, if it happened to stand in
my way.
I couldn't say "Boo" to a man with a gun,

I should run very fast and think it no fun.
If I knew a dog was a-hunting for me,
I should pick up my skirts and away I
should flee.
So thanks for your company, brave Squirrel
and Hare,
I am proud of your friendship, your love and
your care.
(HARE *and* SQUIRREL *stand up and bow to
her, then sit down and continue the meal.*)

   (*A loud rat-tat-tat at the door. They all look
startled and leap to their feet.* HARE *seizes a
chair,* SQUIRREL *takes the poker,* LITTLE GREY
RABBIT *stands alone.* HARE *and* SQUIRREL
take shelter behind her.)

Somebody's knocking! Who can it be?
Somebody's there! Grey Rabbit, do see.
Don't let him in. It may be the Fox
Who'd carry us off in his little tin box.
SQUIRREL (*hiding behind* HARE):
Or a Lion, or a Wolf, or even a Bear
To gobble us up if we didn't take care.
(GREY RABBIT *goes to the door and opens it a
crack, cautiously, then she flings it wide, with
a merry laugh.*)

GREY RABBIT:
It's Old Milkman Hedgehog!
Please leave us a quart.

(HEDGEHOG *enters, with a yoke over his shoulders, and two pails of milk. He wears a white smock, through which the prickles poke. Round his neck is a red scarf.* GREY RABBIT *fetches a jug from the dresser,* HARE *and* SQUIRREL *sit down and continue their breakfast.* HEDGEHOG *pours out the milk, and then stands, looking very important.*)

HEDGEHOG (*speaking slowly*):
    You ought to know, Miss,
    I'm sure that you ought.
    You ought to know . . .
HARE (*impatiently*):
    To know what, good fellow?
    Don't be so slow.

HEDGEHOG (*impressively, with much pointing and waving*):
   There's a Weasel just come
   To the cottage below.
GREY RABBIT (*interrupting*):
   That broken-down cot
   Where forget-me-nots grow?
HEDGEHOG (*nods*):
   He entered last night,
   In the dead of the night,
   With never a light from glow-worm or star.
   Only the Wise Owl spied him from afar.
(GREY RABBIT, SQUIRREL *and* HARE *murmur* "*Wise Owl*".)
   I saw him this morning
   As daybreak was dawning.
   He carried a knife.
   I was scared for my life.

He's a dark, savage fellow
With a waistcoat of yellow,
And very sharp teeth.
I don't think it's safe
To walk on the heath.

SQUIRREL (*alarmed*):

A Weasel, you say?
Come to live in that cot?
Oh! what shall we do?

HARE (*bravely*):

I don't care a jot.
I'm a very brave Hare.
I shall run like the deer
When I see a wild Weasel.
There's nothing to fear.

SQUIRREL:

I could climb up a tree, or run up a post.

HEDGEHOG:

He'd catch you and grill you, Miss Squirrel,
on toast.

GREY RABBIT:

    I should shiver and shake, I very much fear

    If I saw, at the door, a Weasel appear.

    I am much afraid I should quiver with fright

    If a Weasel appeared at the door in the night.

HEDGEHOG (*jerkily*):

    Take my advice. Don't go out.

    Don't go to market with Weasel about.

    Shut the door and turn the key,

    Bolt it and lock it before you have tea.

    Now I must go, I must hurry away

    To warn all the creatures at work or at play,

    To keep in their houses and shut all

    their doors,

    Or the Weasel will get them

    and bite off their paws!

(HEDGEHOG *hurries off.* GREY RABBIT *locks and bolts the door. They sit at the table, shivering and shaking,* HARE *with trembling hands, spilling his tea.*)

HARE:

Fetch me the tongs, and get me a stick.
Hurry, Grey Rabbit. Be quiet, be quick!
(GREY RABBIT *runs to the fire for the tongs, and to the umbrella stand for a stick, and gives them to* HARE.)

HARE:

I'm not at all f-f-f-frightened,
I don't care a j-j-j-j-jot
For w-w-w-Weasels or
w-w-w-Woozels,
If my t-t-t-tea is but h-h-h-hot.
(*Drinks noisily.*)

SQUIRREL:

I have no f-f-fear
When the p-p-poker is near.
I shall take it to bed,
Put it under my head.

24

I have no f-f-fear!

GREY RABBIT (*putting down her cup, and speaking earnestly*):

Someone must go
To the market tomorrow.
I say it with sorrow,
The larder is bare.
It's Friday tomorrow,
Can you go, Hare?

SQUIRREL and HARE (*together, rapidly*):

You must go, Rabbit,
We haven't the habit
Of buying the carrot, the lettuce and bread.
So you must go, Rabbit,
And we'll wait here instead.
You do the shopping, our little grey friend.
You take the purse with the money to spend.

GREY RABBIT (*appealing to* SQUIRREL):

O Squirrel, with ease
You can run up the trees.
O tell me you'll go to the market tomorrow.

SQUIRREL and HARE (*together, crossly*):
    We repeat it with sorrow,
    We haven't the habit,
    O stupid Grey Rabbit,
    Of buying the radish, the nuts and
    the cheese.
    You must go, if you please.
GREY RABBIT (*sorrowfully*):
    I'm rather a coward.
    I'll do as you wish
    But the Weasel may eat me.
    I'll take him a dish
    Of hot macaroni
    And a plate of fried fish
    To serve him instead.
    Then I'll buy the carrot, the lettuce,
    the bread.
    I'm sure it is sweeter
    To eat macaroni
    Than to nibble the bones
    Of a little grey coney.

SQUIRREL and HARE (*patting her back and shaking her paw*):
Well spoken, Grey Rabbit.
We knew you were brave!
The hot macaroni
Our lives may save!

CURTAIN

SCENE TWO

SCENE: *The kitchen next morning. The table is cleared.* SQUIRREL *and* HARE *sit by the fire.* HARE *is dressed in blue coat and red tie.* SQUIRREL, *as before, in spotted dress.*

GREY RABBIT *enters, wearing her red tippet, blue cloak and goloshes. She carries a basket on her arm, with the macaroni and fish covered with a white cloth.* SQUIRREL *is knitting.* HARE *is reading a book with a bright cover. They take no notice of* GREY RABBIT.

27

GREY RABBIT:

Good-bye, dear Squirrel,
Good-bye, my dear Hare.
I'm off to the market.
I'm off to the Fair. (*Dabs her eyes with her apron.*)

SQUIRREL:

You needn't be frightened,
There's nothing to fear.

HARE:

I'll lend you my hanky
To dry up your tear. (*Takes a big red hanky from his pocket and gives it to* GREY RABBIT.)

SQUIRREL:

I'll give you a penny to buy a nice bun. (*Gives penny.*)

HARE:

And don't hurry back, just stay and have fun.

SQUIRREL:

Ride on the roundabout, swing on the swing,
Shy at the coconut, dance in the ring.

GREY RABBIT (*sadly*):

Good-bye, my dear Squirrel.
Adieu, my dear Hare.
I'll bring you back something
Very nice from the Fair. (*Goes out.*)

SQUIRREL (*excitedly*):

What will she bring us?
Now what do you think?
A ginger-bread man?
Or something to drink?

HARE:

A pennorth of humbugs,
Some sugar and spice,
A little ice cream,
Or a cake would be nice.

SQUIRREL:

    She might get a ribbon
    To tie up my tail,
    A pretty blue trifle,
    She'd buy at the sale.

HARE:

    If she brought me some music,
    Or the last latest song,
    Or a flute or a pipe,
    She couldn't go wrong.

SQUIRREL:

    Will you sing to me, Hare,
    While she's gone to the Fair?
    Your voice is so sweet,
    It is always a treat,
    To hear music so gay
    At the dawn of the day,
    To hear music so bright
    In the dark of the night.
    Will you sing? Will you sing?

(HARE *sings and* SQUIRREL *listens. They are sitting in their chairs, with their backs to the door. Music for* HARE'S *song at end.*)

HARE'S song:

There once was a Hare, as I've heard tell,
I've heard tell, I've heard tell;
There once was a Hare, as I've heard tell,
All on a Friday morning.

He dropped a bucket in the Wishing Well,
Wishing Well, Wishing Well,
He dropped a bucket in the Wishing Well,
All on a Friday morning.

He lowered the bucket deep, deep, down,
Deep, deep, down, deep, deep, down;
He brought up a frog striped green
and brown,
All on a Friday morning.

He dressed the frog in cap and gown,
Cap and gown, cap and gown;
He sent her off to the market town
All on a Friday morning.
(WEASEL'S *face appears at window.*)

On the way she saw a mouse,
Saw a mouse, saw a mouse;
Peeping from a wooden house,
All on a Friday morning.

The mouse held up some bits of cheese,
Bits of cheese, bits of cheese;
She said, "I'm in prison for eating these,"
All on a Friday morning.

(*The door opens slowly, and the* WEASEL *creeps in. He wears a yellow waistcoat and black coat, and he carries a thick stick and some rope.* HARE *continues to sing*):
"My house it is a little trap,
Little trap, little trap;
I was caught when the door went down with a snap,"
All on a Friday morning.

(*The* WEASEL *springs on them both, puts a rope round them and drags them off. They squeal and squeak, and the Weasel stuffs dusters into their mouths. As they go, he sings a verse in a very gruff voice.*)

And I am a Weasel, you can see,
You can see, you can see;
Squirrel fried and Hare will be
My breakfast in the morning.
(WEASEL *goes out, dragging them after him.*
The stage is empty, but we can hear GREY
RABBIT *singing in the distance.*

GREY RABBIT enters, stepping daintily. She
speaks to the two empty chairs, which have their
backs to her. She empties her basket on the table,
holding up each article as she speaks.)

GREY RABBIT:
Oh, Squirrel and Hare, here I come!
Marketing over, and safe at home!
I left the food at the Weasel's house,
Stepping as quiet as the tiniest mouse.

Nobody heard me, nobody came!
I hurried along, adown the lane.
I bought a cake, and I bought a song
For Hare, and a ribbon long
For Squirrel, and carrots red,
Lettuce, radish and currant bread.
Biscuits and sausage, parsley, ham,
Apples and walnuts and strawberry jam.
(*She leans over the chairs, laughing, then gives
a cry, and looks around.*)

Where have you gone, Oh Squirrel,
Oh Hare?
The room is empty, vacant the chair.
What is this mark on the floor I see?
The Weasel's been here. Oh lack-a-
day dee!
(*She wipes her eyes on the red hanky.*)
He's taken my darlings, my comrades true!
I'll hurry off after and rescue you.
(*She runs through the door.*)

CURTAIN

SCENE THREE

SCENE: *The Weasel's house. A gloomy room, with window at back. Ragged black curtains, a heap of bones on the window-sill, broken chairs, broken dishes, an old rusty kettle on the table. Fireplace back on left, with big oven. A tall cupboard door on right. Outside door, centre back. Hare and Squirrel lie on the floor, covered by a sack. The Weasel pokes the fire with a long iron poker, and throws more sticks on.*

WEASEL:

I've had hot macaroni,
And a plate of fried eel.
Now some Squirrel and Hare
Will complete the good meal.
I must heat up my oven.

And roast them with care.
I *love* a fat Squirrel,
And *adore* a plump Hare.
I must have currant jelly.
(*Goes to cupboard.*)
And some sour apple sauce.
(*Puts jelly in jampot on table.*)
I must pick some crab-apples
To make it, of course.
I've tied them up tight
They cannot get loose.
I'd as lief have that Hare
As a farmyard goose. (*Goes out.*)

(GREY RABBIT *slips in and looks about her.*
SQUIRREL *and* HARE *shuffle and groan.*)

GREY RABBIT (*agitatedly*):
Are you there?
Squirrel and Hare? (*Stoops down to the sack
and helps them out.*)
Let me hide you.
Take care! Beware!
Don't make a sound!
Don't breathe a word!
You might be found,
You might be heard. (*Peeps through door.*)

Weasel is there.
He's coming back! (*Shuts the two in
the cupboard.*)

I will hide here
Under this sack. (*Lies under the sack.*)

WEASEL (*with crab-apples in hands, returns*):
  Are you ready for dinner? (*Kicks sack.* GREY
  RABBIT *squeaks loudly.*)
  Are you ready for tea? (*Kicks sack
  again. Squeaks.*)
  I will eat you for dinner
  With macaronee.
  With apples and jelly,
  And gravy so good,
  They will smell my nice dinner
  All over the wood.
  They'll all want to share it
  But they'll be too late.
  I shan't leave a bone
  Or a scrap on my plate.
  The Fox and his family
  Would each like a bite,
  But I shan't leave a morsel
  Of dinner tonight.

(Kicks sack again, and GREY RABBIT *squeaks.*
He goes to the oven and opens the door, and
puts his head inside.)

WEASEL:
I think that the oven
Is just about hot.
'Twill perfectly cook them.
I wish I'd the lot.
The Squirrel, the Hare and that Rabbit
so meek,
Would make me a dinner to last me a week.
The Squirrel, Grey Rabbit and fat Mr Hare,
Would give roastings, and stewings, and
lashings to spare.

(GREY RABBIT, *who has crept up behind him,
gives him a push, and shuts the oven door upon
him. He yells, and then is silent.*)
GREY RABBIT:
In you go! In you go!
Wicked old Weasel, the animals' foe.
Stay there, old rascal!
You'll make a fine roast!
You can stop till you're done.
There's no need to boast.
You've had your last dinner,
You shall not eat Hare.
It's Grey Rabbit who's cooked *you*,
So Weasel, beware!

(SQUIRREL *and* HARE *come jumping out of the
cupboard, take hands, and dance round* GREY
RABBIT; *then they stand with her
between them.*)

SQUIRREL:
　　Grey Rabbit, Grey Rabbit,
　　Our lives you have saved.
　　You've caught that bad Weasel,
　　And not been afraid.
　　You've entered his house,
　　His sharp teeth you have braved.
HARE:
　　You shall rest in the parlour
　　And twiddle your paws,
　　You shall bask in the garden
　　And eat out of doors,
　　And feed upon sugar, strawberries
　　and cream,
　　And never go shopping
　　But live like a Queen.
GREY RABBIT:
　　Thank you, my darlings,
　　Dear Squirrel and Hare.
　　We'll all live together
　　With never a care.

There'll be Hedgehog and Moldy-warp,
Fuzzypeg too.
The Speckledy Hen
In her bonnet of blue.
Wise Owl and Water Rat,
All will be there,
With Squirrel, Grey Rabbit,
And brave Mr Hare.

CURTAIN

HARE'S SONG

There once was a Hare, as I've heard tell,
I've heard tell, I've heard tell;
There once was a Hare, as I've heard tell,
All on a Friday morning.

He dropped a bucket in the Wishing Well,
Wishing Well, Wishing Well,
He dropped a bucket in the Wishing Well,
All on a Friday morning.

He lowered the bucket deep, deep, down,
Deep, deep, down, deep, deep, down;
He brought up a frog striped green and
brown,
All on a Friday morning.

He dressed the frog in cap and gown,
Cap and gown, cap and gown;
He sent her off to the market town
All on a Friday morning.

On the way she saw a mouse,
Saw a mouse, saw a mouse;
Peeping from a wooden house,
All on a Friday morning.

The mouse held up some bits of cheese,
Bits of cheese, bits of cheese;
She said, "I'm in prison for eating these,"
All on a Friday morning.

My house it is a little trap,
Little trap, little trap;
I was caught when the door went down
with a snap,
All on a Friday morning.

WEASEL *sings:*
And I am a Weasel, you can see,
You can see, you can see;
Squirrel fried and Hare will be
My breakfast in the morning.

HARE'S SONG

There once was a Hare, as I've heard tell,

I've heard tell, I've heard tell, There

once was a Hare as I've heard tell All

on a Fri - day morn - ing.

48